Contents

A NOTE FROM THE AUTHORS

We have compiled the following information and suggestions in order to assist you in making the best use of this new collection of songs. For quick reference and ease of use, we have divided the titles into various categories of theme, presentation and age suitability, and trust that they will help you get 'maximum mileage' from your music.

DRAMA
Life is a wonderful thing
Spring chicken
The chocolate song
Don't forget (mothers' day song)
Celebrate
Risen!

DANCE
Spring chicken - *costume dance*
Easter jubilation - *jewish style*
Now spring is here - *country dance*
The gift of life - *rap routine*
He's alive! - *ribbon dance*

RE / EASTER PLAY
Hosanna - *Palm sunday / miracles of Jesus*
Easter jubilation - *general celebration*
Mary's song - *reflections on Good Friday*
When I think about the cross - *worship*
Celebrate - *Easter Sunday*
Risen! - *Easter Sunday and beyond*
He's alive! - *Ascension Day, looking ahead*

SCIENCE
Seed song
Spring chicken
Now spring is here
The gift of life

YOUNGER CHILDREN
Seed song
Spring chicken
Celebrate
Hosanna
When I think about the cross

LIFE IS A WONDERFUL THING

1   I woke up this morning - got out of my bed,
Looked in the mirror and I got myself dressed.
With a stretch and a yawn and a scratch of my head
"Life is a wonderful thing" I said,
"Life is a wonderful thing!"

CHORUS   *My heart is beating, morning 'til evening,*
I've got the breath of life inside.
My heart is dreaming, I've got the feeling,
It's so lovely when you know you're alive!

2   I went out this morning, and what did I see?
Buds and blossoms and the birds in the trees.
With a skip and a whistle, a thought came to me,
Life is a wonderful thing indeed,
Life is a wonderful thing!

CHORUS

3   I stayed in this morning, with little to do.
Mum said "Son, you'd better tidy your room".
Then a friend came to see me, and I was excused, (Phew!)
Life is a wonderful thing, it's true,
Life is a wonderful thing!

CHORUS

4   I woke up this morning and here's what I thought,
"What surprises will I find at my door?"
With a new day before me, and plenty in store,
Life is a wonderful thing for sure,
Life is a wonderful thing.
    Life is a wonderful thing, uh huh,
    Life is a wonderful thing!

LIFE IS A WONDERFUL THING

Words & Music: Mark & Helen Johnson

With energy ♩.=132

1.I woke up this mor-ning, got
went out this mor-ning, and

out of my bed, looked in the mir-ror and I
what did I see?__ buds and bloss-oms and the

got my-self dressed. With a stretch and a yawn and a
birds in the trees. With a skip and a whis-tle a

scratch of my head,___ "Life is a won-der-ful thing"
thought came to me,___ "Life is a won-der-ful thing

I said,___ "Life is a won-der-ful thing!"
in deed,___ Life is a won-der-ful thing!

1-3

4.

Fine

I said, "Life is a won-der-ful thing!"_____

CHORUS

My heart is beat-ing, mor - ning 'til eve - ning,

5

3. I stayed in this morning with little to do,
   Mum said "Son, you'd better tidy your room".
   Then a friend came to see me, and I was excused (Phew!),
   Life is a wonderful thing, it's true, life is a wonderful thing.

4. I woke up this morning, and here's what I thought:
   "What surprises will I find at my door?"
   With a new day before me, and plenty in store,
   Life is a wonderful thing, for sure, life is a wonderful thing.
   Life is a wonderful thing, uh huh, life is a wonderful thing!

THE SEED SONG

[handwritten: Y1+2   Plant a very fast growing seed - Jacks beanstalk - Explore pitch low to high climbing up beanstalk.]

1   Find a little seed,   *(Find a little seed)*
      Plant it in the ground,   *(Plant it in the ground)*
      Wait for it to grow,   *(Wait for it to grow)*
      Don't disturb it.
      Don't expect to see,   *(Don't expect to see)*
      Changes overnight,   *(Changes overnight)*
      If you wait a while,   *(If you wait a while)*
      You'll find new life.

      CHORUS   *Sunshine will come,*
                       Raindrops will fall.
                       Your little seed will grow again.
                       Soon there will be a day in Spring when
                       Your seed blossoms and grows.

2   Find a seed of love   *(Echo)*
      Plant it where you can.
      Wait for it to grow,
      Don't disturb it.
      Don't expect to see,
      Changes overnight,
      If you wait a while,
      You'll find new life.

      CHORUS

3   Instrumental

      CHORUS

THE SEED SONG

Words & Music: Mark & Helen Johnson

Very simply ♩.=128

1.Find a lit – tle seed,___
2.Find a seed of love,___

(find a lit – tle seed),___ Plant it in the ground,
(find a seed of love),___ Plant it where you can,

(plant it in the ground) Wait for it to grow, (wait for it to grow)
(plant it where you can)___ Wait for it to grow, (wait for it to grow)

your lit – tle seed will grow a- gain!___ Soon there will be, a

day in Spring when your seed blos – soms and grows.

grows.

and that's that!

10

SPRING CHICKEN!

1   One mother hen sat on **4** little eggs,
Keeping them warm in her little egg nest.
Then one day she heard a crack
And a little voice said, as the egg was hatched:

    CHORUS   *"I'm.... a.... spring chicken!*
I'm yellow and small.
My feathers are fluffy and they're keeping me warm.
My legs are not long, so I'll never be tall,
But I'm a real spring chicken and I'm having a ball!!
(Chicken I'm a chicken, I'm a havin' a ball!)"

2   One mother hen sat on **3** little eggs,
Keeping them warm in her little egg nest.
Then one day she fell asleep
And a little voice said in a whispered tweet:

    CHORUS

3   One mother hen sat on **2** little eggs,
Keeping them warm in her little egg nest.
Then one day she moved about
And a little voice said, as a chick popped out:

    CHORUS

4   One mother hen sat on **1** little egg,
Keeping it warm in her little egg nest.
Then one day she gave a sigh
And a little voice said "SURPRISE! SURPRISE!!"

    CHORUS

SPRING CHICKEN

Words & Music: Mark & Helen Johnson

Cheekily

1. One moth – er hen sat on four lit – tle eggs,
2. One moth – er hen sat on three lit – tle eggs,

keep – ing them warm in her lit – tle egg nest. Then one day she
keep ing them warm in her lit –tle egg nest. Then one day she

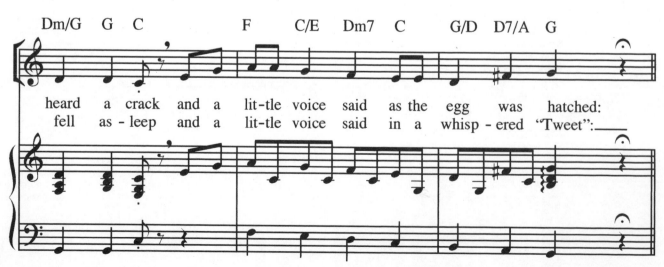

heard a crack and a lit–tle voice said as the egg was hatched:
fell as – leep and a lit–tle voice said in a whisp – ered "Tweet":____

CHORUS

"I'm a SPRING CHICK - EN! I'm yell-ow and small,—— my

feath-ers are flu - ffy and they're keep-ing me warm. My

legs are not long, so I'll nev er be tall, but I'm a real spring chick-en and I'm

last time

hav - ing a ball!! chick - en I'm a chick - en I'm a

13

hav - in' a ball!

3. One mother hen sat on two little eggs,
    Keeping them warm in her little egg nest.
    Then one day she moved about
    And a little voice said, as a chick popped out:

    CHORUS

4. One mother hen sat on one little egg,
    Keeping it warm in her little egg nest.
    Then one day she gave a sigh
    And a little voice said "SURPRISE! SURPRISE!"

    CHORUS

HOSANNA!

1   Who spoke words of wisdom and life?
       Only the one they call Jesus
    Understood what people are like,
       Nobody other than him.
    Who performed miraculous signs?
       Only the one they call Jesus
    Healed the sick, gave sight to the blind,
       Nobody other than him.

    CHORUS   Hosanna! Hosanna!
                 (Rejoice!)
                 Praise him, come praise him!
                 (Sing praise!)
                 Hosanna! Hosanna!
                 (Rejoice!)
                 Lift up your voices and sing!
                 (Lift up your voices and sing!)

2   Who took children into his arms? *(Only the one etc,...)*
    Spoke to storms and made them be calm. *(Nobody other etc,...)*
    Who raised Lazarus up from the dead?
    Made a feast of fishes and bread.

    CHORUS

3   Who made friends with people despised?
    Turned the water into good wine.
    Who got people following him?
    Changed their lives, forgave all their sin.

    CHORUS TWICE

HOSANNA!

Words & Music: Mark & Helen Johnson

Punchy and positive ♩=162

1. Who spoke words of wis - dom and life?__
2. Who took chil - dren in - to his arms?_
3. Who made friends with peo - ple des - pised?

On - ly the one they call Je - sus. Un - der-stood what peo
Spoke to storms and made
Turned the wa - ter in-

ple are like, No-bo-dy oth - er than him.
them be calm,
- to good wine,

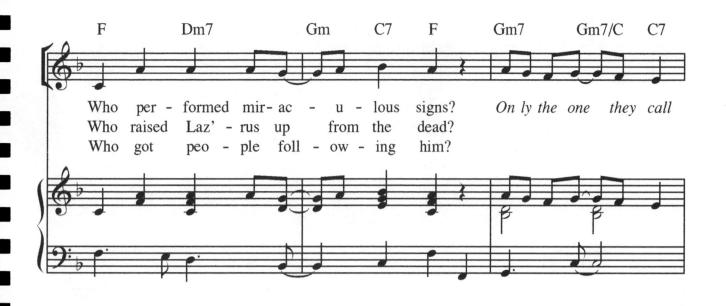

Who per - formed mir - ac - u - lous signs? *On ly the one they call*
Who raised Laz' - rus up from the dead?
Who got peo - ple foll - ow - ing him?

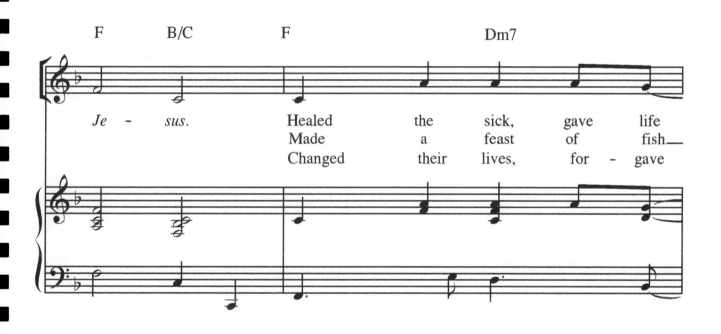

Je - sus. Healed the sick, gave life
Made a feast of fish
Changed their lives, for - gave

to the blind? *No - bo - dy oth - - er than*
es and bread?
all their sin?

CHORUS

18

EASTER JUBILATION!

1   Easter jubilation fills the streets and towns,
    Celebrations have begun.
    Hear the music and the dancing now,
    Join the laughter and the fun!

    CHORUS   *OH! - Raise a joyful shout!*
    Clap your hands and dance - let your feelings out.
    OH! - Hear what it's about,
    Christ the Lord has come to set us free!

2   Put aside your sorrows, wipe your tears away,
    For a better time will come.
    There's a promise of a brighter day,
    Join the laughter and the fun!

    CHORUS

3   La, la, la, la, la, etc,....
    (Dance and Clap)

    CHORUS

4   Easter jubilation fills the streets and towns,
    Celebrations have begun.
    Hear the music and the dancing now,
    Join the laughter and the fun!

    CHORUS TWICE
    (Repeat last line second time round)

EASTER JUBILATION

Words & Music: Mark & Helen Johnson

With pace ♩=138

1.Eas - ter jub - il - at - ion fills the streets and towns,
2.Put as - ide your sorr - ows, wipe your tears a - way,

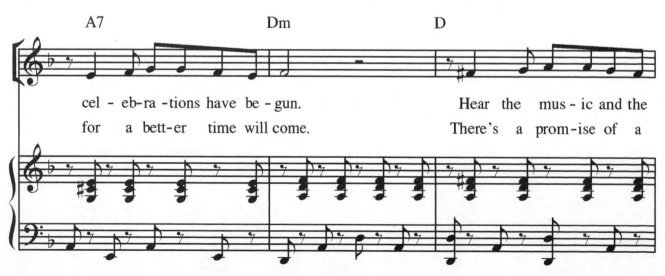

cel - eb-ra -tions have be - gun.   Hear the mus - ic and the
for a bett-er time will come.   There's a prom -ise of a

21

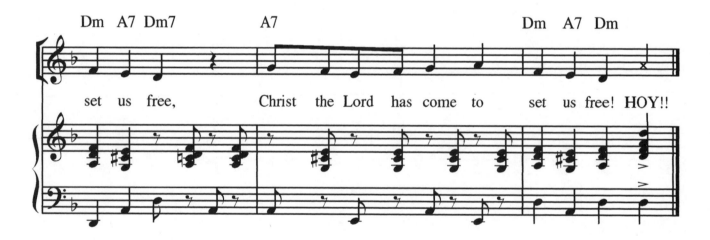

3. La, la, la, la, la, etc,.. (Dance and Clap)

CHORUS

4. Easter jubilation fills the streets and towns,
   Celebrations have begun.
   Hear the music and the dancing now,
   Join the laughter and the fun!

CHORUS TWICE (Repeat last line to end)

NOW SPRING IS HERE

1   Springtime - is laugh and sing time,
It's joining in time, let's give a cheer!
Join hands - and have a fun time,
Enjoy the sunshine, now spring is here.

    CHORUS   *Wake up - the sun is shining*
The earth is smiling, the air is clear.
Blue skies are up above me,
It's really lovely, this time of year.

2   Listen - the birds are singing,
A new beginning is in the air.
Shake off - that winter feeling
And go freewheelin', now spring is here.

    CHORUS

3   Over - the pretty meadows
The green and yellows are everywhere.
Flowers - of every colour,
Can be discovered, now spring is here.

    CHORUS

4   Springtime - is laugh and sing time,
It's joining in time, let's give a cheer!
Join hands - and have a fun time,
Enjoy the sunshine, now spring is here.
    Now spring is here, *now spring is here*, etc,...

NOW SPRING IS HERE

Words & Music: Mark & Helen Johnson

Light and bouncy ♩=120

1.Spring - time is laugh and sing time, it's join - ing
2.List - en, the birds are sing - ing, a new beg -

in time, let's give a cheer! Join hands, and have a
-inn - ing is in the air. Shake off that wint - er

Last time to coda

fun time, en - joy the sun - shine, now spring is here.
feel - ing, and go free - wheel - in' now spring is here.

CHORUS

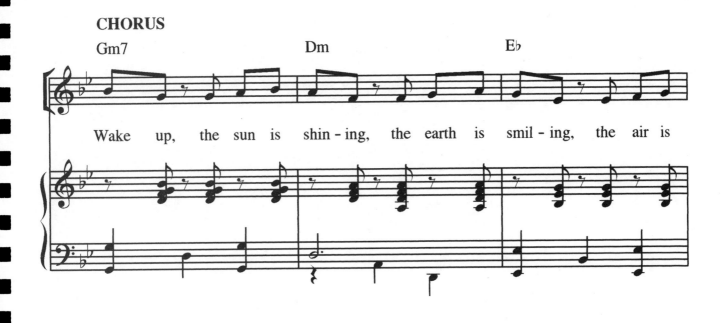

Wake up, the sun is shin - ing, the earth is smil - ing, the air is

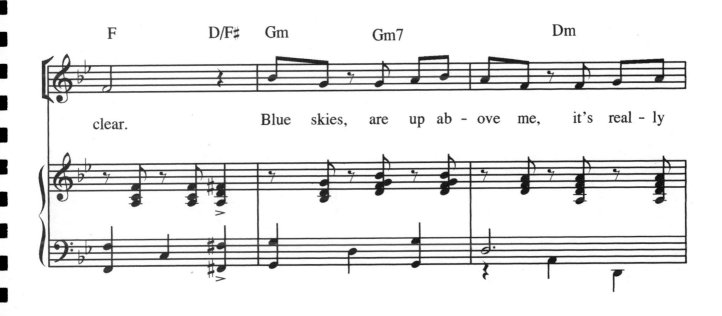

clear. Blue skies, are up ab - ove me, it's real - ly

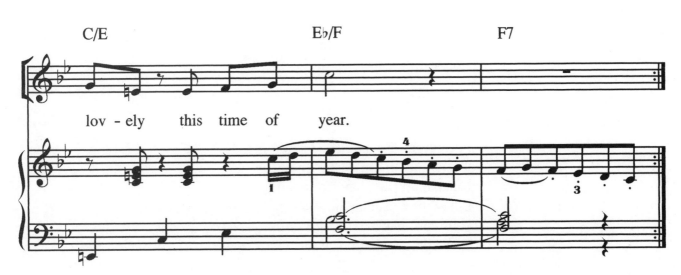

lov - ely this time of year.

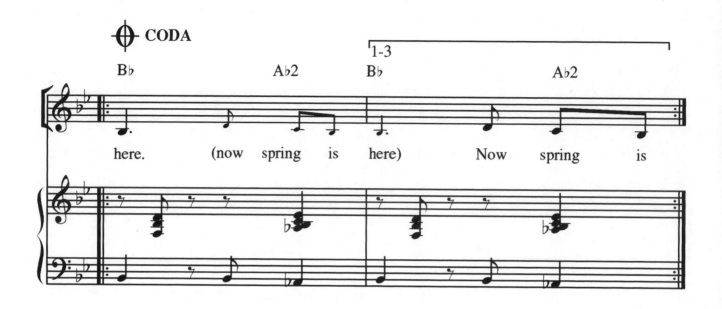

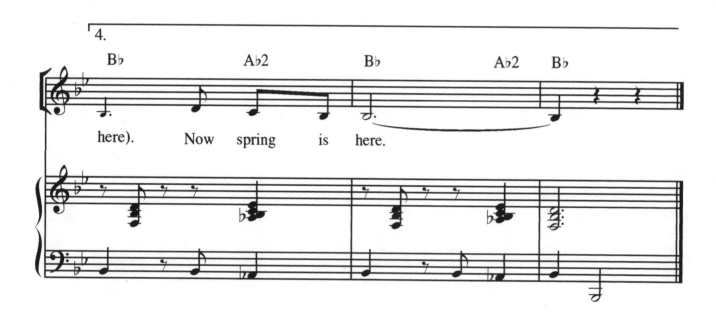

3. Over the pretty meadows,
   The green and yellows are everywhere.
   Flowers of every colour
   Can be discovered, now spring is here.

   CHORUS

4. Springtime - is laugh and sing time,
   It's joining in time, let's give a cheer!
   Join hands - and have a fun time,
   Enjoy the sunshine, now spring is here,
   Now spring is here,.... now spring is here,....
   Now spring is here,.... now spring is here,....

26

THE CHOCOLATE SONG

CHORUS
Oh I've got - lots of chocolate,
Give me - lovely chocolate,
It's the best thing to eat, for sure.
When I get - eggs for Easter
It's my fav'rite treat so I can
Always make some room for more!

1   I've got some plain and milk ones, and some toffee-filled ones,
    I've got boxes all around the place.
    I've got a strong affection for my chocolate collection,
    I'm mad about that chocolate taste!

CHORUS

2   I've eaten milky-white ones and the sweets inside them,
    (I've got chocolate all round my face!)
    They all had pretty wrappers, but that's not what matters,
    I'm mad about that chocolate taste!

CHORUS

3   I've had some sickly sweet ones, and some pretty cheap ones,
    But I couldn't see them go to waste.
    I s'pose I should know better, but it's nearly Easter,
    I'm mad about that chocolate taste!

CHORUS TWICE

THE CHOCOLATE SONG

Words & Music: Mark & Helen Johnson

With a 'country' feel ♩=126

CHORUS

Oh I've got lots of choc'-late, give me, love-ly choc'-late, it's the best thing to eat for sure. When I get eggs for Eas-ter it's my fav'-rite treat so I can al-ways make some room for

DON'T FORGET!   (Mother's Day Song)

1   Don't forget to tell your Mum you love her,
Give her a hug when you get home.
Don't forget to tell your Mum that she's the best,
Make her put her feet up - she deserves a rest!
Don't forget to tell your mum you love her -
> *She does all the washing, the cleaning, the shopping,*
> *And all because she loves us so!*

2   Don't forget to tell your Mum you love her,
Give her a hug when you get home.
Don't forget to thank her for the things she does,
Looking after everyone without a fuss!
Don't forget to tell your Mum you love her -
> *She takes and collects us, and makes us our breakfast,*
> *She does all the washing, the cleaning, the shopping,*
> *And all because she loves us so!*

3   Don't forget to tell your Mum you love her,
Give her a hug when you get home.
Don't forget to give her something really nice,
It's the thought that matters, not the size or price!
Don't forget to tell your mum you love her -
> *She helps and advises, she gives us surprises,*
> *She takes and collects us, and makes us our breakfast,*
> *She does all the washing, the cleaning, the shopping,*
> *And all because she loves us so!*

4   Don't forget to tell your Mum you love her,
Give her a hug when you get home.
Don't forget to help your Mum with all the chores,
Clean your bedroom like you've never done before!
Don't forget to tell your Mum you love her -
> *She puts up with rugby, she knows when to hug me,*
> *She helps and advises, she gives us surprises,*
> *She takes and collects us, and makes us our breakfast,*
> *She does all the washing, the cleaning, the shopping,*
> *And all because she loves us so!*

31

DON'T FORGET
(Mothers' Day Song)

Words & Music: Mark & Helen Johnson

make her put her feet up she de -serves a rest!
look - ing af - ter ev' - ry - one with - out a fuss!
it's the thought that mat - ters not the size or price!

Don't for - get to tell your mum you love her, she
Don't for - get to tell your mum you love her, she

.§. **CHORUS**

1.

Last time to coda

does all the wash-ing, the clean-ing, the shop -ping, and

all be cause she loves us so!

33

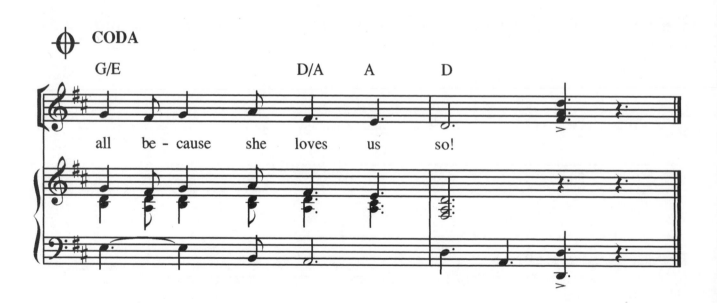

4. Don't forget to tell your mum you love her,
   Give her a hug when you get home.
   Don't forget to help your mum with all the chores,
   Clean your bedroom like you've never done before.
   Don't forget to tell your mum you love her -

MARY'S SONG

1 I look to the hillside, the skies have turned grey,
This place is deserted, where love was betrayed.
The life you gave freely was taken from me today.

2 I see it so clearly, the look on your face,
The sadness and sorrow, the pain you embraced.
And now it's all over, a silence enfolds the day.

CHORUS *Tell me why did it have to be done,*
When my feelings of love are so strong?
Could it be there's a reason for taking the life of my son?

3 The noises still echo around in my head,
The shouts and the jeering, the crowds as they fled.
But now it's all over, and I'm on my own again.

4 I gratefully bore you, I watched as you grew,
I listened and wondered at all that you knew,
But this is the hardest of all that I've learned from you.

CHORUS TWICE

MARY'S SONG

Words & Music: Mark & Helen Johnson

36

be there's a rea- son for tak-ing the life__ of my son?

3. The noises still echo around in my head,
   The shouts and the jeering, the crowds as they fled.
   But now it's all over, and I'm on my own again.

4. I gratefully bore you, I watched as you grew,
   I listened and wondered at all that you knew.
   But this is the hardest of all that I've learned from you.

WHEN I THINK ABOUT THE CROSS

When I think about the cross
When I think of Jesus,
I'm reminded of his love -
Love that never leaves me.
Who am I
That he should die,
Giving life so freely?
When I think about the cross
Help me to believe it.

Dedicated to Stanley and Doreen Voke

WHEN I THINK ABOUT THE CROSS

Words & Music: Mark & Helen Johnson

When I think a-bout the cross, when I think of Je - - - sus, I'm re-min- -ded of his love, love that nev - er

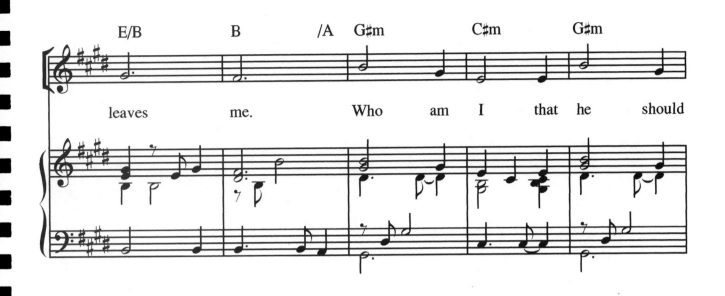

E/B   B   /A G#m   C#m   G#m

leaves   me.   Who   am   I   that   he   should

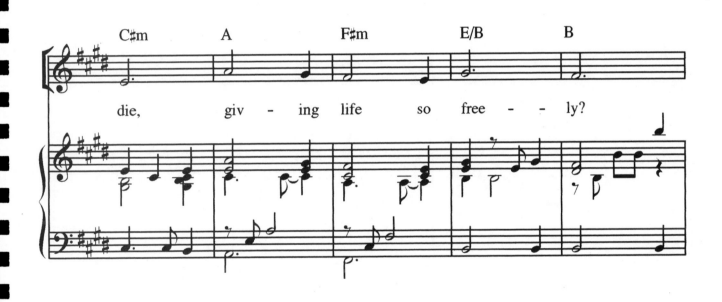

C#m   A   F#m   E/B   B

die,   giv – ing   life   so   free – – ly?

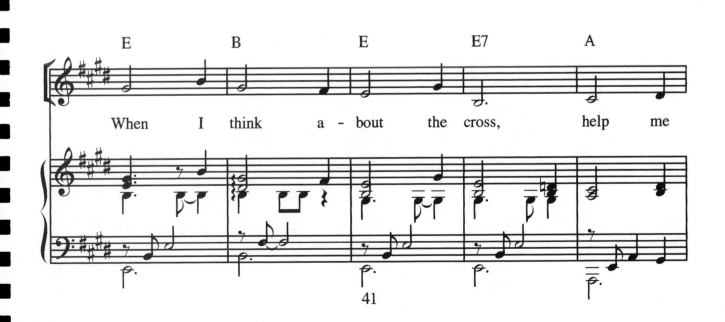

E   B   E   E7   A

When   I   think   a – bout   the   cross,   help   me

41

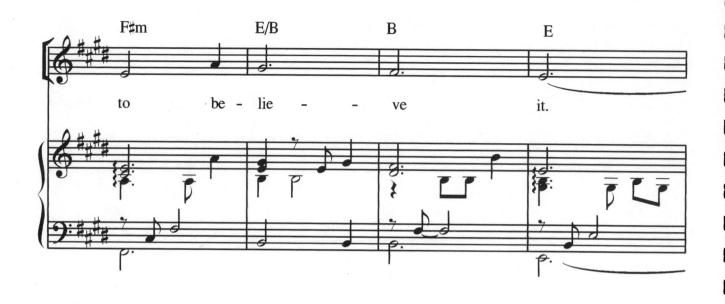

to be - lie - - ve it.

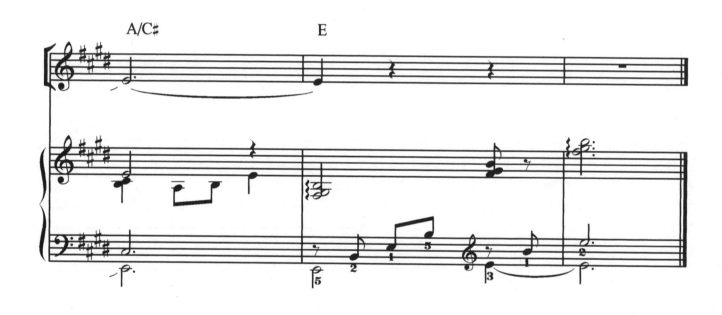

CELEBRATE!

1   Sing a song, sing a joyful song,
     Sing a joyful song to celebrate! (Repeat)

     CHORUS   *Jesus is alive, you know,*
               He's risen from the dead. (OH YEAH!)
               He was crucified but now he's
               Risen like he said! (HALLELUJAH!)

2   Clap your hands, clap your hands like this,
     Clap your hands like this to celebrate! (Repeat)

     CHORUS

3   Jump up and down, up and down and around,
     Up and down and around to celebrate! (Repeat)

     CHORUS

4   Dance to the beat, to the beat of the drum,
     To the beat of the drum to celebrate! (Repeat)

     CHORUS

5   Wave your hands, wave your hands in the air,
     Wave your hands in the air to celebrate! (Repeat)

     (Cheer, clap, stamp, shout, CELEBRATE!!)

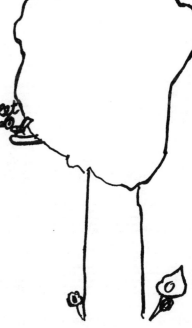

CELEBRATE!

Words & Music: Mark & Helen Johnson

CHORUS

Jes - sus is a-live, you know, He's ris - en from the dead!_

He was cru - ci - fied but now he's ris - en like he said.

CODA

(Hall - e - lu - jah!) joy - ful song to cel - e - brate!

4. Dance to the beat, to the beat of the drum,
   To the beat of the drum to celebrate! (Repeat)

5. Wave your hands, wave your hands in the air,
   Wave your hands in the air to celebrate! (Repeat)

6. Sing a song, sing a joyful song,
   Sing a joyful song to celebrate! (Repeat)

RISEN!

CHORUS   *Risen! Risen! Jesus is - risen!*
               The Spirit was given - Jesus is alive!
               Risen! Risen! Jesus is - risen!
               The Spirit was given - Jesus is alive!

1   Early in the morning on the first day of the week,
      Women went to visit at the tomb.
      Angels came and told them, "The one you've come to see,
      He isn't here, but you will meet him soon!"

      CHORUS

2   Fearful and excited, amazed by all they'd seen,
      Mary and her friends ran from the tomb.
      Finding the disciples together where they'd meet,
      Bursting with joy, they ran into the room!

      CHORUS

3   Two of the believers, with thoughts about the week,
      Walked the road so lonely and confused.
      While they spoke of Jesus, and all he'd come to mean,
      He came along beside them with the news:

      CHORUS

4   All of his disciples were terrified to see
      Jesus there before them in the room.
      "Why are you so frightened?" he said "It's really me!
      All of the things I told you have come true!"

      CHORUS

      Risen! Risen! Jesus is risen!

RISEN!

Words & Music: Mark & Helen Johnson

47

48

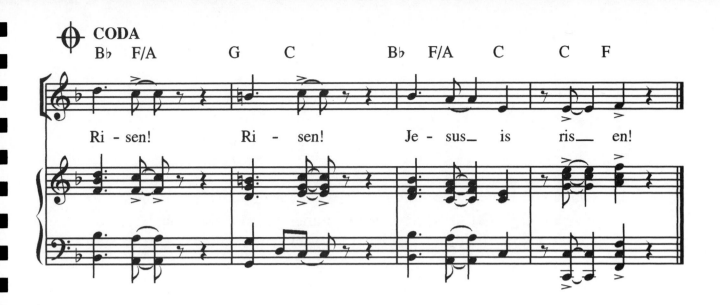

CODA

Ri – sen! Ri – sen! Je – sus__ is ris__ en!

3. Two of the believers, with thoughts about the week,
   Walked the road so lonely and confused.
   While they spoke of Jesus, and all he'd come to mean,
   He came along beside them with the news:

CHORUS

4. All of his disciples were terrified to see,
   Jesus there before them in the room.
   "Why are you so frightened?" he said "It's really me!
   All of the things I told you have come true!"

CHORUS

Risen! Risen! Jesus is risen!

49

THE GIFT OF LIFE

1   Have you <u>ever</u> stopped to question what goes <u>on</u> inside your body?
I've a <u>notion</u> that some complicated <u>things</u> go on inside you.
If you <u>take</u> a bit of time just to <u>wonder</u> why, you'll <u>discover</u> there are
reasons why we're <u>feeling</u> so alive!!
My <u>heart</u> is beating, my <u>lungs</u> are breathing,
My <u>brain</u> is ticking over - it's a <u>real</u> good feeling!
My <u>pulse</u> is rising, I'm <u>en</u>ergising!
The <u>muscles</u> in my arms and legs are <u>busy</u> exercising!

        CHORUS   *The gift of life is upon us all*
                         The gift of life is upon us all.

2   <u>Listen</u> to me people what I'm <u>saying</u> is true, it's a <u>matter</u> of importance
that I'm <u>telling</u> to you, 'cause if <u>living</u> is for loving then you'll <u>only</u> feel
alive when you <u>give</u> yourself to others with a <u>love</u> that's long and
wide, so <u>give</u> it!! <u>Give</u> it a go! <u>Give</u> a little love and then you'll <u>really</u>
know:
It's <u>all</u> about caring, it's <u>all</u> about sharing,
'Cause <u>love</u> for one another is for <u>giving</u> and for getting.

        CHORUS   *The gift of life is upon us all*
                         The gift of life is upon us all.

3   I <u>got</u> some good advice from my <u>father</u> and my mother when they <u>told</u>
me that in life there is <u>plenty</u> to discover. There are <u>places</u> to go, -
<u>choices</u> to make - I'll <u>tell</u> you this for nothing you can <u>learn</u> from your
mistakes, so
<u>Don't</u> be a bore, <u>go</u> for more. <u>There's</u> a world around you and it's <u>there</u>
to be explored.
<u>Don't</u> stop looking, <u>don't</u> stop learning. <u>Make</u> the most of living while
the <u>earth</u> is still turning.

Cont'd.

4   I <u>know</u> it's very easy to get <u>caught</u> up in a hurry and we'll <u>always</u> have our problems and a <u>fair</u> old share of worries. But <u>stop</u> for a minute, - and <u>you</u> will realise, there are <u>things</u> we take for granted every <u>day</u> of our lives:
<u>Sights</u> to behold, <u>sounds</u> to be heard, a <u>world</u> that's packed with colour full of <u>music</u> and words.
<u>Food</u> and drink, <u>games</u> and toys. <u>Things</u> to be experienced and <u>plenty</u> to enjoy.

CHORUS   *The gift of life is upon us all*
                  The gift of life is upon us all. (Repeat)

5   It's <u>amazing</u> when you think of all the <u>people</u> on the earth, that there's <u>no-one</u> who could ever be <u>exactly</u> like yourself. So there's <u>no</u> point in comparing - you'll <u>never</u> really live 'til you <u>come</u> to see that you have something <u>quite</u> unique to give.
<u>Heart</u> and mind, <u>soul</u> and strength, can <u>all</u> be used together in a <u>life</u> that's well-spent.
Make the <u>most</u>, of what you've <u>got</u>, - 'cause <u>all</u> that you've been given is a <u>gift</u> from God!

Make the <u>most</u> of what you've <u>got</u>, - 'cause <u>all</u> that you've been given is a <u>gift</u> from God! (Repeat)

...The title and many of the ideas for this song were provided by the children in Year 6 at Ashford Park Primary School in Middlesex, in response to the question: "What does it mean to be alive?". Thank you!

Please note that all the <u>underlined</u> words are to be accented on the first beat of the bar

THE GIFT OF LIFE

Words & Music: Mark & Helen Johnson

The gift of life

is up - on us all.

We are providing notation of the chorus only - Effective performance of this rap will require use of the backing track

THANK YOU FOR LOVING ME

1   Before you made the skies and sea
      Your heart was full of love for me.
      You knew the person I would be,
      Thank you for loving me.

2   You came to earth to live like us,
      With words of life, and arms of love.
      You showed the way to heav'n above,
      Thank you for loving us.

      CHORUS   *Thank you Jesus,*
                          Thank you my Lord.
                          Your love came down from heaven
                          Come fill up my heart evermore.

3   Because God loved the world so much
      You paid the price for all of us.
      You gave your life upon a cross,
      Thank you for loving us.

4   INSTRUMENTAL

      CHORUS

5   So thank you Lord for loving me
      Today and all eternity.
      And may my song forever be
      "Thank you for loving me".

      CHORUS TWICE

THANK YOU FOR LOVING ME

Words & Music: Mark & Helen Johnson

⊕ CODA

-fill   up   my   heart___   ev - er - more.

3. Because God loved the world so much,
   You paid the price for all of us.
   You gave your life upon a cross,
   Thank you for loving us.

   CHORUS

4. So thank you Lord for loving me,
   Today and all eternity,
   And may my song forever be
   "Thank you for loving me".

   CHORUS TWICE

HE'S ALIVE!

CHORUS   *Come and join in the song,*
Jesus Christ is Lord over all
And he lives to reign forevermore,
The heavens applaud, "He's alive!" - "He's alive!"

Lift your hearts and your voices,
Fill the earth with rejoicing for

1   He's ascended to the skies
In heaven now he reigns.
Lord of glory, Lord of life
He will return again!

    CHORUS

2   Every knee shall bow to him
And every one confess:
Jesus Christ is Lord and King
He's conquered sin and death!

    CHORUS

3   Every nation, every tribe
Will glorify his name.
All creation shall bow down
And honour him with praise!

Come and join in the song,
Jesus Christ is Lord over all
And he lives to reign forevermore,
The heavens applaud, "He's alive!"

HE'S ALIVE!

Words & Music: Mark & Helen Johnson

Triumphantly ♩. = 62

CHORUS

Come and join in the song, Je-sus Christ is Lord ov-er all, and he lives to reign for-ev-er more, the heav-ens app-laud: "He's a-live!"

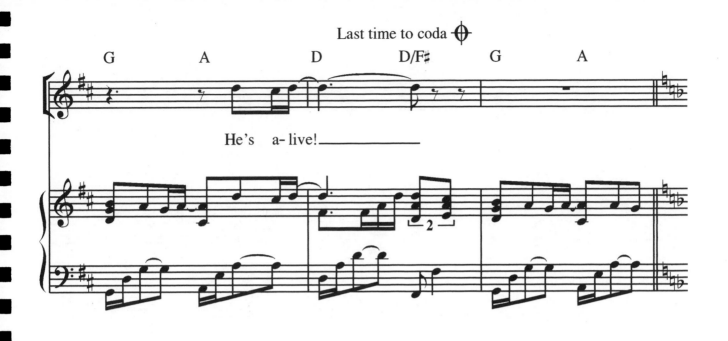

Last time to coda ⊕

He's a-live!

Lift your hearts and your voi - ces, fill the

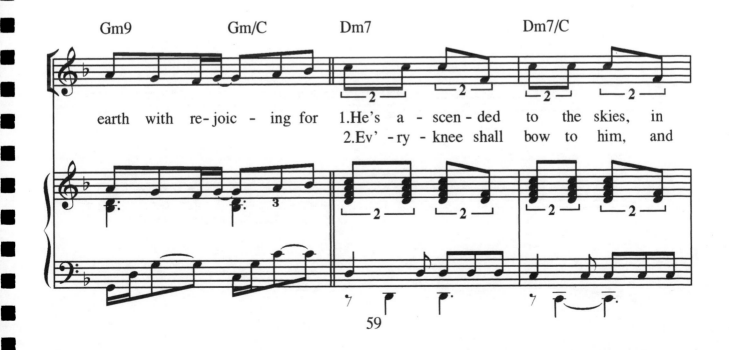

earth with re-joic-ing for
1. **He's a-scen-ded to the skies, in**
2. **Ev'-ry-knee shall bow to him, and**

heaven now he reigns.
ev'ry one con - fess:_____

Lord of glory,
Je - sus Christ is

Lord of life, he will re - turn a - gain!
Lord and King, he's con-quered sin and death!

CODA

He's a - live!_____

60

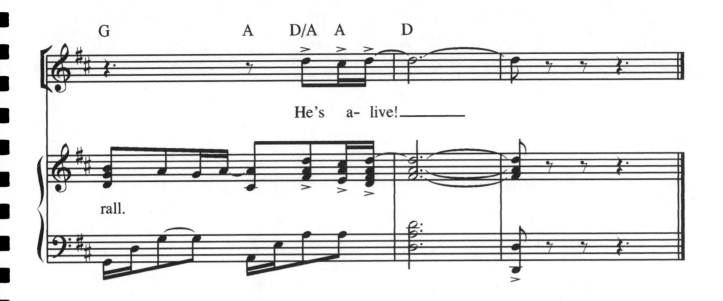

He's a-live!____

rall.

3. Every nation, every tribe,
   Will glorify his name.
   All creation shall bow down
   And honour him with praise!

more superb songbooks from

OUT OF THE ARK MUSIC

The popular 'EVERY' series of songbooks

season   **day**   **christmas**   **easter**

Each package in the series will provide you with:

- 15 original songs - catchy, memorable and great fun to sing!
- Piano music, melody and chords
- Photocopiable lyric sheets
- Cassette with all songs sung by children (side 1)
- Professionally arranged backing tracks for rehearsal and performance (side 2)
- A tremendous resource for assemblies, topic work <u>and</u> concerts

**The 'EVERY' series - popular with children, music advisors and
non-specialists alike!**

Send for details to:
OUT OF THE ARK MUSIC
The School House, 15 Esher Green, Esher, Surrey, KT10 8AA
Tel (01372) 463274   Fax: (01372) 463351

ALSO AVAILABLE....

off to bethlehem

An exciting nativity musical comprising 9 catchy songs, which can be used individually or as a whole. Easy-to-use package includes teacher tips, stage directions, piano music, percussion parts, lyric sheets for photocopying.

This has proven to be one of the most popular publications in the Out Of The Ark Music catalogue.

Especially suitable for ages 5-9

it's a baby!

The christmas story with a difference! Told from the perspective of a weary innkeeper who finds he's in for a sleepless night. 9 new songs perfectly suited to younger voices, without compromising on musical quality. Simple rhyming narrative links and percussion parts are provided.

Funny, melodic and <u>very</u> singable!

Written specifically for 3-7 year olds

witnesses *by Margaret Carpenter*

Many years after the 'first' Christmas, Mary and Joseph, shepherds, kings, angels and stars all come back together as witnesses to the great event.

7 delightful songs, easy to learn and great fun to sing. Part-singing made surprisingly simple!

Best suited to ages 6-11

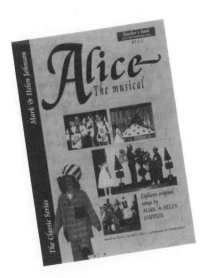

This timeless classic is now retold as a great new musical!

18 excellent songs in a wonderful variety of musical styles. Top quality package includes 96-page teacher's book (piano music, lyric sheets, casting tips, ideas for staging, props, etc), double cassette/CD with full backing tracks included. Full script also available.
Ideal for children aged 7-14

MARK & HELEN JOHNSON are a husband and wife team who have been writing music together since 1985. In 1990 they received private sponsorship which allowed them to leave their full-time employment and devote themselves to developing their musical skills. Prior to this, Mark had been in music retail sales, and Helen was a primary school teacher specialising in music and english.

In 1991 they formed **OUT OF THE ARK MUSIC**, a Surrey-based company, which enabled them to publish, promote and distribute their own material. Their songbooks have been used in over 6,000 schools to date, and continue to be in popular demand throughout the British Isles and beyond,

Mark and Helen continue to work very closely with primary schools by running music composition workshops for 5-11's (KS 1-2), advising teachers on the implementation of music in the National Curriculum, and contributing to educational publications. Their popularity with non-specialists and music advisors alike, is bringing in a growing number of enquiries and letters of appreciation. They are currently working on a new collection of songs in the EVERY series, as well as a nursery/infants songbook.

If you would like further information about the courses that Mark & Helen run, or would like to receive a sample pack of their work, please write to them at the address on the previous page. They would be very happy to receive any suggestions or comments about their publications.

January 1998